SINGING, DANCING CARPENTER

a musical

SINGING, DANCING CARPENTER

a musical

Text and lyrics by Michael Forster
Music by Christopher Tambling

Kevin Mayhew

We hope you enjoy *Singing, Dancing Carpenter*.
Further copies are available from your local music shop or Christian bookshop.

In case of difficulty, please contact the publisher direct:

The Sales Department
KEVIN MAYHEW LTD
Rattlesden
Bury St Edmunds
Suffolk IP30 0SZ

Phone 0449 737978
Fax 0449 737834

Please ask for our complete catalogue of outstanding Church Music.

First published in Great Britain in 1993 by Kevin Mayhew Ltd.

ISBN 0 86209 370 8

Cover design by Roy Mitchell.
Music Editor: Anthea Smith.
Music Setting: Tricia Oliver.

Printed and bound in Great Britain.

Foreword

This is a musical about celebrating life in all its fullness. Implicit in that is a protest against all that is life-denying in our world.

The focus of that, in this work, is Jesus, and the title picks up two things about him which were, according to people's point of view, highly attractive or utterly offensive. One was his festive lifestyle, and the other his comparatively humble station in society. Life, for him, was to be enjoyed and celebrated - and ordinary people were to be helped and encouraged to do so. This meant opposing everything which made life unnecessarily burdensome, especially guilt, prejudice and injustice. In turn, of course, this made him a threat to those who had a vested interest in those phenomena.

The musical divides into three parts. Part One concentrates upon the positive reactions of ordinary people, while Part Two highlights the opposition which was raised, especially in the religious establishment, and which led to the crucifixion. Part Three proclaims the belief that, in the end, life has the last word.

So the challenge to us all, in our present age, is to celebrate life in all its fullness, and to oppose anything which denies it. This means a particular concern for those who are most disadvantaged.

We hope that this musical will be in itself a celebration of life, and enjoyable simply as that. We hope also that it will be a way of enabling us all to make or renew our commitment to the marginalised - of whom there are many in our own society - not as a duty but as a joy. For this reason, the participation of the audience is of the utmost importance. Not only do we have the opportunity to make that commitment; we have also the opportunity to recognise within ourselves the 'priest', the 'pharisee' and the self-righteous, so as to be able to deal with them.

We offer this work in the hope that it will be not only thought-provoking and evangelistic (in the best sense of the word) - but fun!

MICHAEL FORSTER
CHRISTOPHER TAMBLING

Contents

Page

Part One: Acclamation

1. Singing, dancing carpenter 8
Mary Magdalene, Male Solo, Chorus, Audience

2. Water to wine 12
Alto Solo, Tenor Solo, Chorus

3. Isn't this the carpenter? 16
Soprano Solo, Bass Solo, Jesus, Chorus

4. Come as you are 22
'Anna' (a sick woman), Jesus, Chorus

5. Oh! Zacchaeus! 26
Zacchaeus, Chorus of Accusers, Chorus

5a. Oh! Zacchaeus! 32
Solo Voice, Chorus

6. One was a traitor 35
Soprano Solo, Bass Solo

7. Singing, dancing carpenter (2) 40
Solo Voice(s), Chorus, Audience

Part Two: Opposition

8. Isn't this the carpenter? (2) 46
Soprano Solo, Bass Solo, Jesus, Chorus

9. Singing, dancing carpenter (3) 52
Pharisee, Zealot, Priest, Roman Official, Chorus, Audience

10. Stone her! 56
Pharisee, Disciple, Agitator, Onlooker, Jesus, Chorus of Tenors and Basses

11. He's just a simple carpenter   67
    Zealot, Pharisee, Priest, Roman Official, Chorus

12. Cry Hosannah!   70
    Solo Voices, Chorus

13. Crucify Him!   76
    Solo Voice(s), Chorus

14. I do not know the man   82
    Solo Voice, Peter, Male Voices, Chorus

15. What kind of man was this?   87
    Mary Magdalene, Joanna, Chorus

Part Three: Resurrection

16. He's alive   95
    Mary Magdalene, Jesus, Chorus of Women, Chorus of Men

17. Do not touch   105
    Mary Magdalene, Chorus

18. Got to get away (Jerusalem Blues)   108
    'Rachel' (wife of Cleopas), Cleopas, Chorus

19. One hundred and fifty-three   114
    Solo Voice, Chorus

20. Finale: Singing, dancing carpenter (4)   120
    Solo Voice(s), Chorus, Audience

Notes on Performance   124

PART ONE: ACCLAMATION

Narrator 1:	Once upon a time, there was a man called Jesus ...
Narrator 2:	Oh, no! Not religion! Talk about anything else you like, but not religion!
Narrator 1:	All right, then. Once upon a time, there was a singing, dancing carpenter.
Narrator 2:	A what?!
Narrator 1:	A singing, dancing carpenter.
Narrator 2:	That sounds more interesting - what about him?
Narrator 1:	He was in many ways quite an ordinary chap.
Narrator 2:	Yes?
Narrator 1:	Came from an ordinary home.
Narrator 2:	Well?
Narrator 1:	Pursued an ordinary trade.
Narrator 2:	*(Impatiently)* So? Why are you bothering to tell me about him?
Narrator 1:	Because he did some extraordinary things.
Narrator 2:	And is there the remotest danger of your actually telling me what they were?
Narrator 1:	No.
Narrator 2:	*(Thoroughly frustrated)* What d'you mean, 'No'?
Narrator 1:	Well, you told me not to talk about religion.
Narrator 2:	Alright, I give in - just get on with it!
Narrator 1:	Well, he had my problem.
Narrator 2:	You mean, people found him aggravating?
Narrator 1:	Yes - partly.
Narrator 2:	Why?
Narrator 1:	*He* talked about religion, too. The religious authorities got quite upset about it.
Narrator 2:	I'm not surprised. How would he have liked it if they had gone into the carpentry business?
Narrator 1:	That was certainly part of it - but there was more. He loved life, and enjoyed it - and wanted everyone else to enjoy it as well.
Narrator 2:	Well, you can't have religious people actually enjoying themselves, can you?!
Narrator 1:	Quite. People had got so tied up in rules and regulations, not to mention religious ceremonies, that life just wasn't fun any more.
Narrator 2:	So what did he do about it?
Narrator 1:	He made people feel good about themselves - it was like being set free - made them ...
Narrator 2:	Hang on, I've heard enough from you - why not let the people themselves tell me about it?

1. SINGING, DANCING CARPENTER

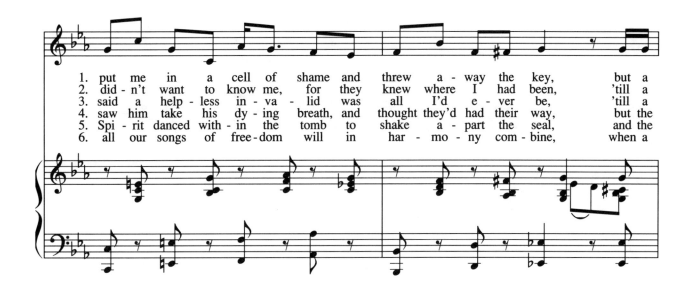

1. put me in a cell of shame and threw a - way the key, but a
2. did - n't want to know me, for they knew where I had been, 'till a
3. said a help - less in - va - lid was all I'd e - ver be, 'till a
4. saw him take his dy - ing breath, and thought they'd had their way, but the
5. Spi - rit danced with - in the tomb to shake a - part the seal, and the
6. all our songs of free - dom will in har - mo - ny com - bine, when a

Refrain
Chorus & Audience

1. sing - ing, danc - ing car - pen - ter broke in and set me free! Let's
2. sing - ing, danc - ing car - pen - ter said, 'I have made you clean!'
3. sing - ing, danc - ing car - pen - ter said, 'Come and dance with me!'
4. sing - ing, danc - ing car - pen - ter had o - ther things to say!
5. sing - ing, danc - ing car - pen - ter con - ti - nued with his reel!
6. sing - ing, danc - ing car - pen - ter turns wa - ter in - to wine!

f

sing with the car - pen - ter a song of li - ber - ty; let's

dance with the car - pen - ter, for all the world to see; let's

learn with the car - pen - ter what God would have us be, and

Verses 1 - 5

la - bour with the car - pen - ter to set cre - a - tion

free!

Male Solo: 2. They
Male Solo: 3. They
Mary Magdalene: 4. They
Mary Magdalene: 5. He
Both: 6. So

mf

mf

10

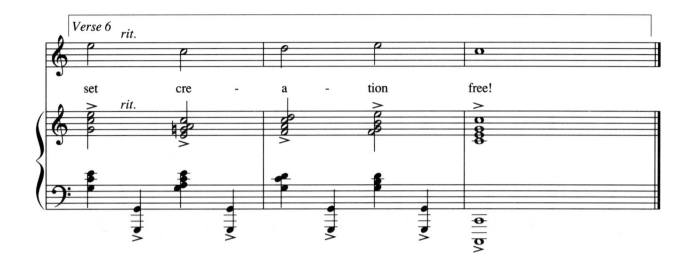

Verse 6 *rit.*

set cre - a - tion free!

Narrator 2:	Water into wine? That's a funny idea!
Narrator 1:	Yes, but that's how it seemed. For centuries, people had had bad religion thrust down their throats -
Narrator 2:	I know the sort of thing: 'Don't do this ... '
Narrator 1:	'Don't do that ... '
Narrator 2:	'And don't even contemplate ... other things.'
Narrator 1:	Quite so. You've obviously encountered it.
Narrator 2:	You can say that again! It's as dull as -
Narrator 1:	Dishwater?
Narrator 2:	Exactly.
Narrator 1:	So if someone came along and convinced you that religion wasn't meant to be like that -
Narrator 2:	It would be a miracle.
Narrator 1:	About on a par with turning dishwater into wine?
Narrator 2:	What's that supposed to mean?
Narrator 1:	Well, just imagine it. People feeling the way you do about religion - told that they were bad, and God wouldn't love them unless they changed ...
Narrator 2:	Sounds pretty standard stuff to me.
Narrator 1:	Then along comes this fellow who enjoys life, and tells people who think they are bad that God loves them - just as they are. And they haven't got to earn it. For those who got the message, it was like dirty water being turned to wine!
Narrator 2:	Now that's a miracle!

2. WATER TO WINE

Ten: 1. Pet - ty res - tric - tions our spi - rits con - fine;
2. Law - yers got hold of the e - dicts di - vine,
3. came to the wed - ding and gave us the sign:
Ten: 4. Je - sus a - dop - ted a heal - thi - er line:
5. 'If you would be a di - sci - ple of mine,

1. life is a wed - ding with - out a - ny wine!
2. turned grace a - round, and made wa - ter from wine!
3. law is the wa - ter, but love is the wine!
4. 'Don't drink their wa - ter, but try the new wine!'
5. don't waste the wa - ter, but turn it to wine!'

Refrain

f

Chorus: Wa - ter to wine is the pro - mise he brings,

✱ S A

f

Wa - ter to wine is the pro - mise he brings,

T B

f

✱ Optional SATB Chorus

13

love with-out rea - son the song that he sings,

love with - out rea - son, the song that he sings,

grace and for - give - ness his na - ture de - fine,

grace and for - give - ness his na - ture de - fine,

guilt turns to free - dom like wa - ter to wine.

guilt turns to free - dom like wa - ter to wine.

Narrator 2:	So, how did he actually go about doing that? - it all sounds great in theory …
Narrator 1:	He began at the synagogue in Nazareth.
Narrator 2:	That's where he came from, isn't it?
Narrator 1:	Yes, he grew up there, and worked there as a carpenter.
Narrator 2:	It must have been fairly easy to get going, then. At least people knew him, and probably respected him.
Narrator 1:	Well, they certainly knew him and that wasn't entirely helpful - but I'll come to that later.
Narrator 2:	Tell me what he did.
Narrator 1:	What would you do, if you wanted to talk to people about their religion?
Narrator 2:	Well, if I wanted that badly enough, then I suppose I'd go to church.
Narrator 1:	If you wanted it badly enough.
Narrator 2:	That's what I said.
Narrator 1:	So that's what Jesus did - except that he was probably a familiar figure there - so they let him preach - and they couldn't believe their ears.
Narrator 2:	You mean he said something terrible?
Narrator 1:	No, quite the opposite. But that was really the problem, at first - they were so busy being amazed by how well he spoke that they didn't pay much attention to what he was saying.

3. ISN'T THIS THE CARPENTER?

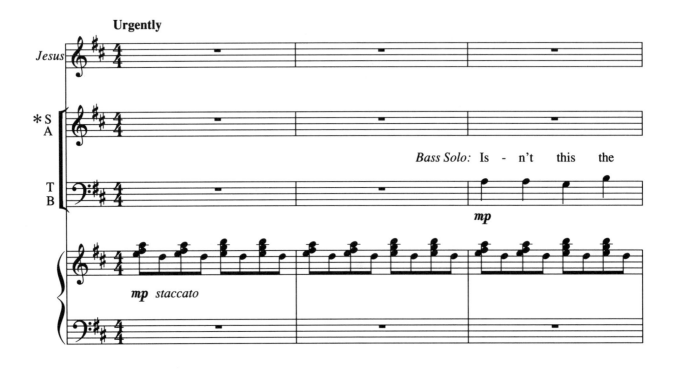

* SATB sections may be sung in unison

18

tell out the gos - pel of free - dom, pro - claim - ing the day of the
vi - sions of jus - tice and mer - cy, to o - pen the eyes of the
this has come true as you hear it, for this is the time and the

Is - n't this the car - pen - ter from

C

Lord.
blind.
place!

Refrain

Na - za - reth? Is - n't this the car - pen - ter? Is - n't this the

son of Jo - seph? Is - n't this the car - pen - ter from Na - za - reth?

Is - n't this the car - pen - ter from Na - za - reth?

Is - n't this the car - pen - ter?

Is - n't this the son of Jo - seph? Is - n't this the

Is - n't this the

car - pen - ter from Na - za - reth?

Narrator 2:	So he said all that, and they didn't even hear him?
Narrator 1:	Eventually, he got through to them - and that's when the trouble started.
Narrator 2:	You mean they took him seriously?
Narrator 1:	Well, I'll come to that later. Let's stay with the positive things for now.
Narrator 2:	He developed quite a following, didn't he?
Narrator 1:	He seems to have become very well known, if that's what you mean - probably because of his way of making very ordinary people feel important - like the woman who touched the edge of his clothing.
Narrator 2:	Why on earth would she do that?
Narrator 1:	Because she was ill and she thought he could cure her.
Narrator 2:	Why did she think that?
Narrator 1:	Because Jesus had a reputation as a miracle-worker.
Narrator 2:	So why didn't she just go and ask him?
Narrator 1:	In those days a lot of sick people were made to feel guilty - and dirty - and especially with the particular kind of illness she had.
Narrator 2:	A bit like some kinds of illness today.
Narrator 1:	That's right - and this woman felt so guilty that she was afraid to approach Jesus.
Narrator 2:	That's odd, considering the kind of person he was.
Narrator 1:	Yes, but people often feel that way, today - for example - why don't you go to church?
Narrator 2:	That's easy - it's full of people who are good - or who think they are - and not at all the place for irreverent characters like me.
Narrator 1:	There you are - a lot of people think like that. The church seems so obsessed with goodness that people are afraid to come near it. So they sort of hang around the edges. That was how this woman felt about Jesus. She didn't dare go to him, so she sneaked up and touched just the edge of his coat.

4. COME AS YOU ARE

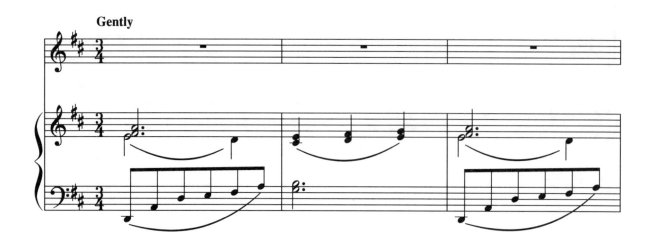

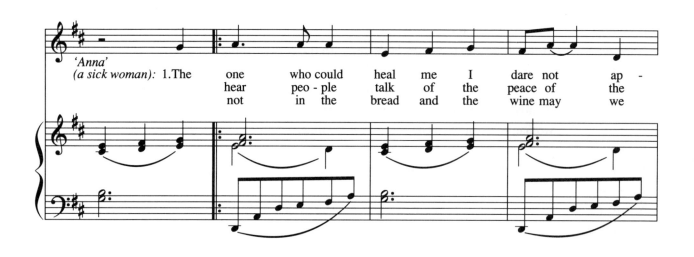

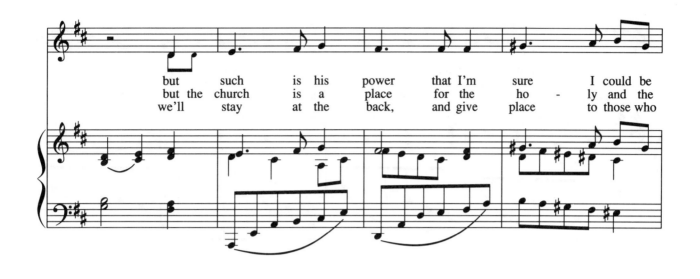

but such is his power that I'm sure I could be
but the church is a place for the ho - ly and the
we'll stay at the back, and give place to those who

healed by the edge of the gar - ment he's wear - ing.
good, and the gos - pel's for those who be - lieve it.
know and can do what the gos - pel's de - mand - ing.

D

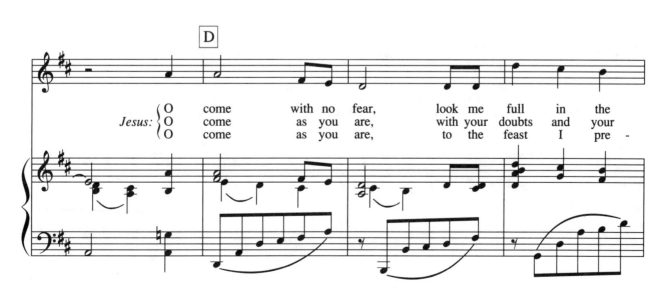

Jesus: { O come with no fear, look me full in the
O come as you are, with your doubts and your
O come as you are, to the feast I pre -

23

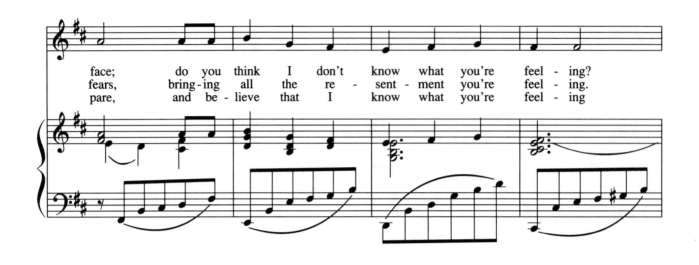

face;   do you think I don't know what you're feel - ing?
fears,   bring-ing all the re - sent - ment you're feel - ing.
pare,   and be - lieve that I know what you're feel - ing

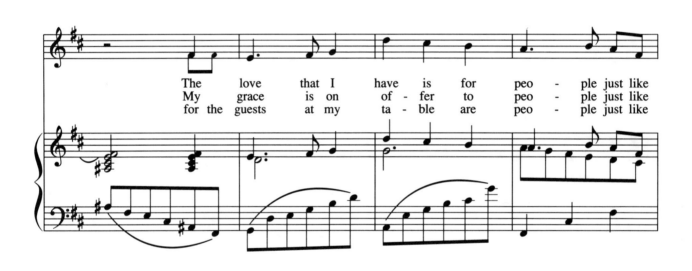

The love that I have is for peo - ple just like
My grace is on of - fer to peo - ple just like
for the guests at my ta - ble are peo - ple just like

E

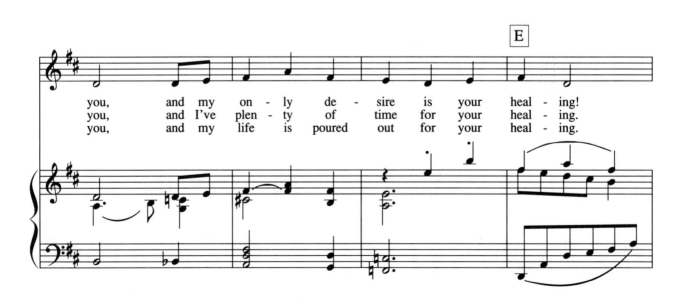

you,   and my on - ly de - sire is your heal - ing!
you,   and I've plen - ty of time for your heal - ing.
you,   and my life is poured out for your heal - ing.

Chorus: 2. We
Chorus: 3. But

Narrator 2:	He sounds like quite a special sort - it's a pity he's not still around.
Narrator 1:	Isn't it just . . . ? *(Pause)* In fact, he really cared about the people who got pushed out of things - even if it was partly their fault. Take Zacchaeus, for example - he was a tax collector.
Narrator 2:	Hey, be careful what you say - there may be some of those here!
Narrator 1:	Well, I think they're rather different now. For one thing, in Jesus' time, Palestine was part of the Roman Empire.
Narrator 2:	What had that to do with it?
Narrator 1:	Tax collectors worked for the occupying power - so many people hated them just for that.
Narrator 2:	And for another thing?
Narrator 1:	Well, for another thing, they were widely thought to be dishonest. They often overtaxed people, and pocketed the difference.
Narrator 2:	Couldn't they have been reported for that?
Narrator 1:	That was the trouble - the Roman governors didn't mind, as long as the taxes were collected.
Narrator 2:	So this Zacchaeus was a pretty unpopular fellow.
Narrator 1:	You can say that again!

5. OH! ZACCHAEUS!

tax us out of house and home, and ne - ver send it

on to Rome; why don't you tax our ve - ry breath, and

charge us du - ty on our death? Oh! Zac - chae - us!

Oh! Zac - chae - us!

Accusers:
1. He
2. He
3. He
4. He
5. What -

mf

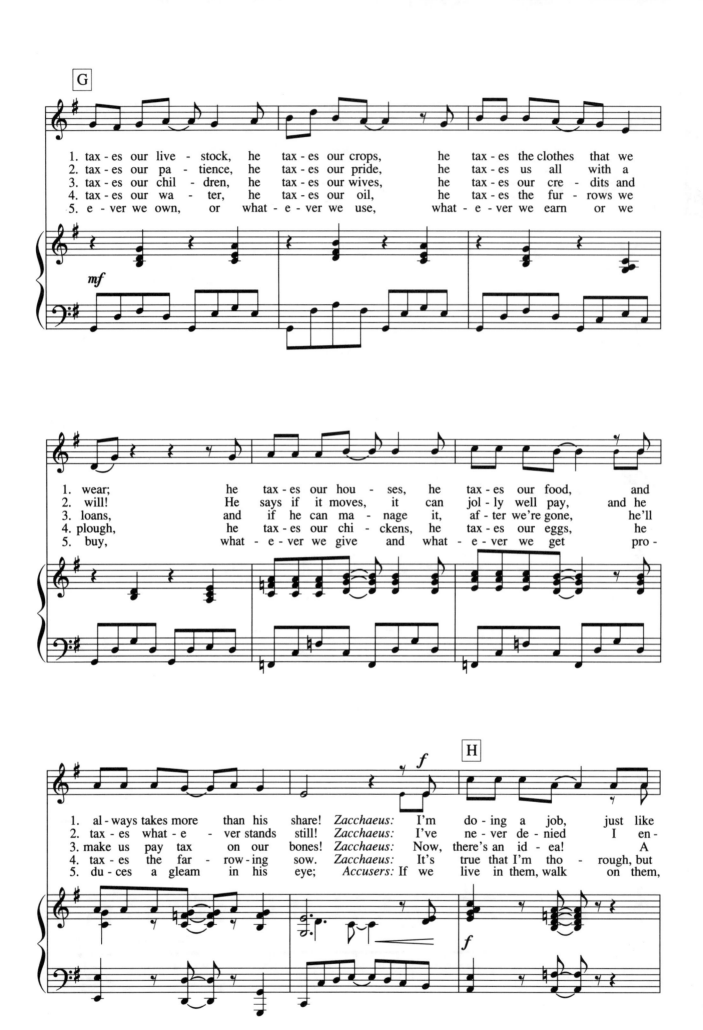

G

1. tax - es our live - stock, he tax - es our crops, he tax - es the clothes that we
2. tax - es our pa - tience, he tax - es our pride, he tax - es us all with a
3. tax - es our chil - dren, he tax - es our wives, he tax - es our cre - dits and
4. tax - es our wa - ter, he tax - es our oil, he tax - es the fur - rows we
5. e - ver we own, or what - e - ver we use, what - e - ver we earn or we

1. wear; he tax - es our hou - ses, he tax - es our food, and
2. will! He says if it moves, it can jol - ly well pay, and he
3. loans, and if he can ma - nage it, af - ter we're gone, he'll
4. plough, he tax - es our chi - ckens, he tax - es our eggs, he
5. buy, what - e - ver we give and what - e - ver we get pro -

H

1. al - ways takes more than his share! *Zacchaeus:* I'm do - ing a job, just like
2. tax - es what - e - ver stands still! *Zacchaeus:* I've ne - ver de - nied I en -
3. make us pay tax on our bones! *Zacchaeus:* Now, there's an id - ea! A
4. tax - es the far - row - ing sow. *Zacchaeus:* It's true that I'm tho - rough, but
5. du - ces a gleam in his eye; *Accusers:* If we live in them, walk on them,

28

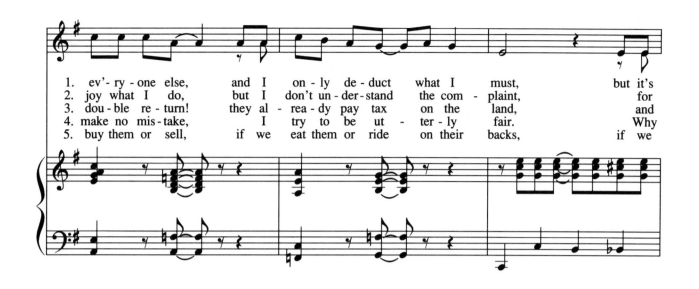

1. ev'-ry-one else, and I on-ly de-duct what I must, but it's
2. joy what I do, but I don't un-der-stand the com - plaint, for
3. dou-ble re-turn! they al - rea-dy pay tax on the land, and
4. make no mis-take, I try to be ut - ter-ly fair. Why
5. buy them or sell, if we eat them or ride on their backs, if we

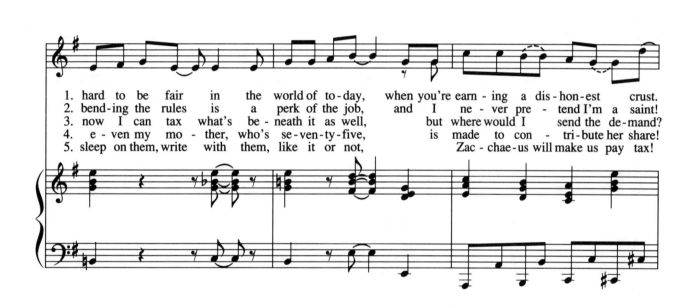

1. hard to be fair in the world of to-day, when you're earn - ing a dis-hon-est crust.
2. bend-ing the rules is a perk of the job, and I ne - ver pre - tend I'm a saint!
3. now I can tax what's be - neath it as well, but where would I send the de-mand?
4. e - ven my mo - ther, who's se-ven-ty-five, is made to con - tri-bute her share!
5. sleep on them, write with them, like it or not, Zac - chae-us will make us pay tax!

Refrain

I

Chorus: Oh! Zac - chae - us! Who will you cheat to - day? Oh!

Zac - chae - us! D'you know what peo - ple say? You charge us tax on

ev' - ry - thing, but you your - self don't pay a thing; you

tax us out of house and home, and ne - ver send it

on to Rome; why don't you tax our ve - ry breath, and

getting more and more angry

charge us du - ty on our death? Oh! Zac - chae - us!

cresc.

shouted

Oh! Zac - chae - us! Oh! Zac - chae - us.

ff

▲

Narrator 2:	I bet Jesus had a thing or two to say to that man!
Narrator 1:	Well, Zacchaeus *was* a tax man, but they didn't have V.A.T. in those days . . .
Narrator 2:	Wake up - I said *that* man - not *VAT* man.
Narrator 1:	Sorry - well, it seems to be the kind of person Jesus was, not his words, which had an impact on Zacchaeus. All Jesus did was invite himself to his home.
Narrator 2:	That's all?
Narrator 1:	I doubt it - but the next thing we know about, Zacchaeus is standing up and making this big announcement - in front of lots of witnesses.
Narrator 2:	What sort of announcement?
Narrator 1:	Apparently, he decided to give half his property away, to the poor, and said that if he had cheated anyone, he would repay them four times over.
Narrator 2:	Wow! How did people respond to that?
Narrator 1:	We don't really know. Jesus was pleased, but as for the rest of the people, we have to guess.
Narrator 2:	Well I hope they believed him, and started being a little kinder to him.

5a. OH! ZACCHAEUS!

Calypso style

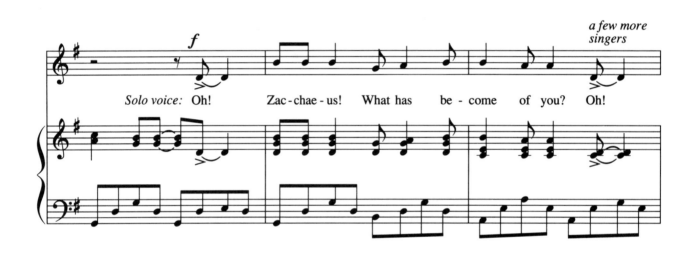

Solo voice: Oh! Zac-chae-us! What has be-come of you? Oh!

a few more singers

Zac-chae-us! What is this thing you do? You say that you'll re-

even more singers

turn four - fold the mo - ney that you wrong - ly hold, and

all your right - ful pro - per - ty you'll split in half for

J

cha - ri - ty? *All:* You seem to be a man re - formed, and

with increasing joy

our o - pi - nion's been trans - formed! Oh! Zac - chae - us!

cresc.

Oh!   Zac - chae - us!   Oh!   Zac - chae - us!

□

Narrator 2:	So those were the kind of people he spent his time with?
Narrator 1:	Certainly were. In fact, he became known as the friend of sinners.
Narrator 2:	A picker-up of fallen women.
Narrator 1:	Well, I would hardly have put it like that. All kinds of people were thought of as sinners. As far as the religious people were concerned, a 'sinner' was anyone they didn't like or approve of.
Narrator 2:	And those were the people Jesus had for his friends?
Narrator 1:	Yes - if society didn't want them, Jesus did.
Narrator 2:	So what went wrong?
Narrator 1:	How d'you mean?
Narrator 2:	Just that - if Jesus was the friend of the people society didn't want, why aren't those people in the churches now?
Narrator 1:	Oh, I see what you mean!
Narrator 2:	Well, all I can say is that when his friends were all around him, it must have been a pretty amazing sight.
Narrator 1:	It must indeed - and you can imagine why Jesus and his friends weren't always welcome, by some people.
Singer:	That's right ...

6. ONE WAS A TRAITOR

*   May be sung by one person throughout or by several people, changing voice at appropriate points.

chat! And one was a was-ter and one was a tramp and

one was con-fined to his bed, and one had a dread-ful in-

fec-tious di-sease, and one had come back from the dead! And

one was a scep-tic and one was a sage, and one was a man with a

cause, and one had a hus-band who worked for the king and

one was a wri-ter of laws. And one was a drea-mer, and

one was a fool and one had a great deal to do. And

one was-n't ve - ry much dif - f'rent from me, and

one was the i-mage of you!

(Repeat until ready for No. 7)

Narrator 2:	What me?
Narrator 1:	Yes, you.
Narrator 2:	You mean there was probably someone like me among his friends?
Narrator 1:	I've no doubt you were represented - and all of those people out there, as well - everyone's in there somewhere. As people, the disciples were remarkably unremarkable!
Narrator 2:	Uncommonly common!
Narrator 1:	Extraordinarily ordinary - but enough of this: what do you think of this Jesus character now?
Narrator 2:	Well, I'm not much of a singer or dancer, but this carpenter seems to have hit the nail on the head.

7. SINGING, DANCING CARPENTER (2)

1. heard a - bout the car - pen - ter, the things he did and said, his
2. see him still a - round the world, where hu - man life is cheap; he
3. sings a song of free - dom with the peo - ple of his choice, and
4. sings a song of pro - test through the beg - gar's out - stretched hand, of

1. love of life and peo - ple, and the hum - ble life he led. And
2. comes to set the cap - tive free and teach the lame to leap, and
3. in his li - be - ra - ting dance, the voice - less find a voice. Where
4. greed and ex - ploi - ta - tion in this 'green and plea - sant land'! And

1. where cre - a - tion still is gripped by dark - ness and des - pair, the
2. where the poor - est peo - ple are en - slaved by guil - ty fears, the
3. peo - ple live in hope, and with a long - ing to be free, the
4. where the card - board hou - ses of the poor of - fend our sight, the

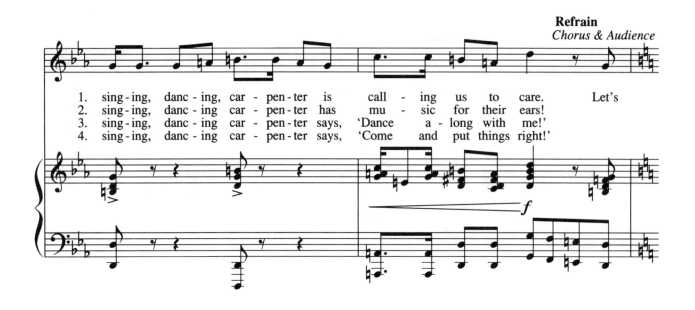

1. sing - ing, danc - ing, car - pen - ter is call - ing us to care. Let's
2. sing - ing, danc - ing car - pen - ter has mu - sic for their ears!
3. sing - ing, danc - ing car - pen - ter says, 'Dance a - long with me!'
4. sing - ing, danc - ing car - pen - ter says, 'Come and put things right!'

sing with the car - pen - ter a song of li - ber - ty; let's

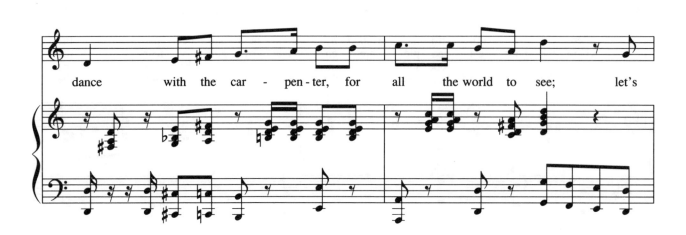

dance with the car - pen - ter, for all the world to see; let's

learn with the car - pen - ter what God would have us be, and

Verses 1 - 3

la - bour with the car - pen - ter to set cre - a - tion

free!

Solo: 2. We
Solo: 3. He
Solo: 4. He

mf

Verse 4 *rit.*

set cre - a - tion free!

rit.

PART 2: OPPOSITION

Narrator 2:	Jesus sounds like a terrific character! But I don't understand: if he was doing all those wonderful things, how did he come to be publicly executed as a criminal?
Narrator 1:	That's the point. For some people, he was not good news. What they regarded as undesirable people were being encouraged to find a place in society. And telling people that God loved them even if they weren't good was seen as an anarchists' charter.
Narrator 2:	That sounds familiar. A lot of people in the church now seem to think it's some sort of a club for good people, and they get very worried if what seem to be the wrong sort of people find their way in.
Narrator 1:	That's true - although you can understand it. We all want security, and we all feel safer with people who conform to our ideas of what's normal.
Narrator 2:	So, a lot of people actually within the church today find this kind of thinking rather threatening.
Narrator 1:	Yes, and you can't entirely blame them. That's what went wrong at Nazareth. The people in the synagogue welcomed Jesus, at first, until they began to realise the implications of what he was saying.
Narrator 2:	Such as what?
Narrator 1:	Such as, if this ordinary carpenter they all know is the Messiah God has promised, he's not what they expected and certainly not what they wanted.
Narrator 2:	What did they expect?
Narrator 1:	They expected someone who would throw out the Romans - a military figure - and Jesus hardly fitted that description.
Narrator 2:	So, because he wasn't what they wanted, they turned against him.
Narrator 1:	Yes. And the same thing happens now. A lot of people still really want a god of power who'll put their enemies in their place, and anyone who tries to tell them otherwise isn't going to win many popularity contests!

8. ISN'T THIS THE CARPENTER? (2)

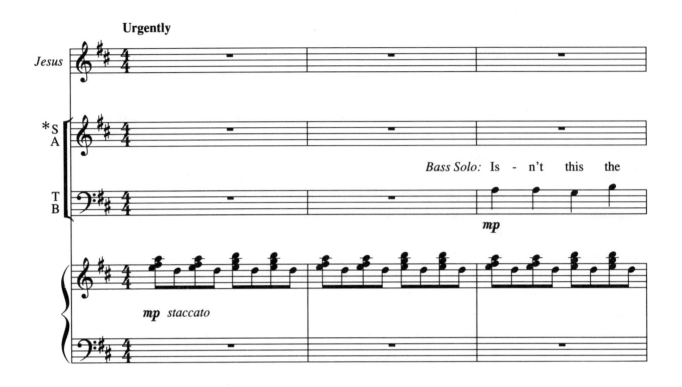

* SATB sections may be sung in unison.

Jesus: { 1.   A
        { 2.   The
        { 3. There were

car - pen - ter from Na - za - reth?

pro - phet is ne - ver res - pec - ted a - mong his im - me - di - ate peers,
poor, the be - reft and the lone - ly in Is - rael, E - li - jah could see,
plen - ty of sick need - ing heal - ing in the place where E - li - sha was known,

Is - n't this the car - pen - ter? Is - n't this the

48

but is gree-ted with scorn and de - ri - sion, through
but he went to an a - li - en peo - ple, whose
but to Naa-man, a Sy - ri - an sol - dier, God's

son of Jo - seph? Is - n't this the

pride and ir - ra - tio - nal fears.
spi - rits at least might be free!
heal-ing com-pas - sion was shown!

Refrain
(with increasing hostility)

car - pen - ter from Na - za - reth? Is - n't this the

car - pen - ter from Na - za - reth?

Narrator 2: Well I can see that he made himself a bit unpopular - but that can't account for the way things turned out - just a bit of local opposition.

Narrator 1: That's the problem - it wasn't just a bit of local opposition. He upset just about every influential group in the country.

Narrator 2: How did he manage that?

Narrator 1: The trouble was that he didn't fit in with what any of them wanted. The pharisees -

Narrator 2: Yes I know - they thought religion was about rules and regulations - and Jesus never had a lot of time for that sort of thing.

Narrator 1: Then there were the zealots - the rebels. They wanted a liberator who would throw out the Roman occupiers. At first they thought Jesus was just the job.

Narrator 2: So what went wrong?

Narrator 1: He didn't do what they wanted. They needed to stir up hatred and resentment, and Jesus talked about love and forgiveness - hardly the fuel for a revolution!

Narrator 2: No, I can see that. So who else was there?

Narrator 1: There were the priests.

Narrator 2: Ah - the priests. I bet they supported him.

Narrator 1: Actually, they didn't like him either. You see, they had a nice cosy arrangement with the Roman Governor. They didn't interfere in politics, and he let them have a quiet life and keep all their privileges and their wealth.

Narrator 2: So, how did Jesus interfere with that?

Narrator 1: Well, I suppose it must have been alarming for them to hear Jesus talking about the kingship of God. The Romans certainly weren't going to like it, and they might start cracking down. So the priests had good reason to be worried.

Narrator 2: Which brings us to the Romans.

Narrator 1: That's right. To be honest, the Romans weren't all that concerned to begin with, but the others managed to convince them that Jesus was a threat.

Narrator 2: So they ended up with an unholy alliance between four groups of people who normally couldn't stand the sight of each other.

Narrator 1: Yes. Human nature hasn't changed much, has it!

9. SINGING, DANCING CARPENTER (3)

Deliberately

mf

Pharisee: 1. Re -

1. li - gion is a so - lemn thing, with ri - tu - als and rules; God
2. Ro - mans were our mas - ters, and we took a lot of pain, but,
3. had a good ar - range - ment with the go - vern - ment in Rome: we
4. were their be - ne - fac - tors, if they on - ly re - a - lised; with

1. on - ly loves the ho - ly, and he's got no time for fools! As
2. come the re - vo - lu - tion, we'd have had them out a - gain. We
3. kept God out of po - li - tics; they left our faith a - lone. But
4. Ro - man peace and Ro - man roads, we made them ci - vi - lised. Yet,

Refrain
Chorus & Audience

1. guar-dians of the truth, we kept the peo-ple in their place, 'till a
2. nee-ded a Mes-si-ah of a fierce and war-like kind; was a
3. Je-sus threa-tened all of that, and peo-ple could not see that a
4. ne-ver were they sa-tis-fied; we gave them ev'-ry-thing, but a

1. sing-ing, danc-ing car-pen-ter came preach-ing love and grace. We'll
2. sing-ing, danc-ing car-pen-ter the best that God could find?
3. sing-ing, danc-ing car-pen-ter was all he'd e-ver be.
4. sing-ing, danc-ing car-pen-ter they wan-ted for their king!

si - lence the car-pen-ter; for once we all a-gree! We'll

ri - di-cule the car-pen-ter for ev'-ry one to see. We'll

say that the car - pen - ter's not all he claims to be; we'll

Verses 1 - 3

cru - ci - fy the car - pen - ter, and then we'll all be

mf

free!

Zealot: 2. The
Priest: 3. We
Roman Official: 4. We

mf

Verse 4

then we'll all be free!

Narrator 2:	So, let me get this straight. Because Jesus enjoyed life, and because he was from a fairly ordinary background, a lot of ordinary people liked him. But, for precisely those same reasons, a lot of other people didn't - and they wanted him out of the way.
Narrator 1:	That's a pretty good summary of it.
Narrator 2:	Well, since it was the powerful people who were against him, surely all they had to do was pick him up and deal with him. After all, it was not exactly a democracy, was it - so you'd have thought they could do whatever they liked.
Narrator 1:	It wasn't that simple. Even in non-democratic countries - sometimes especially there - the privileged people are afraid of what would happen if the ordinary people ever really got going. That's why there's so much repression.
Narrator 2:	So you're saying that the authorities would have liked to put Jesus out of the way, but were afraid of a riot, or something?
Narrator 1:	They were afraid, either way. If they left him alone, and let him go on giving the people ideas about freedom and justice, there would be trouble. But if they tried to stop him, while he was at the height of his popularity, then that might trigger something off.
Narrator 2:	So what they needed to do was to discredit him.
Narrator 1:	Got it in one. That's why they kept on setting up awkward situations for him.
Narrator 2:	Oh? Such as what?
Narrator 1:	Once, they brought a woman to him whom they'd caught in the act of adultery.
Narrator 2:	How embarrassing!
Narrator 1:	Yes, but never mind that. They thought they'd put Jesus into a dilemma.
Narrator 2:	Dai who? Is he connected with Dai Jones from Swansea?
Narrator 1:	Di-*lemma!* They thought they'd give him an impossible choice.
Narrator 2:	You mean like between Turkish delight and hazelnut whirls?
Narrator 1:	Hardly. You see, according to the Jewish law which Moses had given them, any one found committing adultery should be stoned to death.
Narrator 2:	A bit extreme, I'd say - but where's the problem?
Narrator 1:	Well, Israel was an occupied country - and the Romans wouldn't allow them to execute anybody. So, if Jesus said 'Yes' to stoning her, he'd get arrested for inciting a riot.
Narrator 2:	That's easy, then - he had to say 'No'.
Narrator 1:	And then he'd have been showing disrespect to the law of Moses, and the people would turn against him.
Narrator 2:	Mmm - tricky - either way, they'd got him.
Narrator 1:	That's what they thought, too. So they brought her to Jesus.

10. STONE HER!

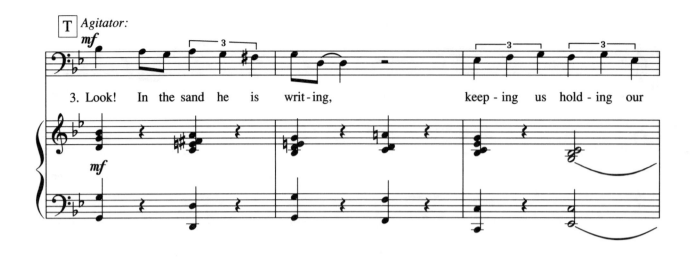

3. Look! In the sand he is writ-ing, keep-ing us hold-ing our

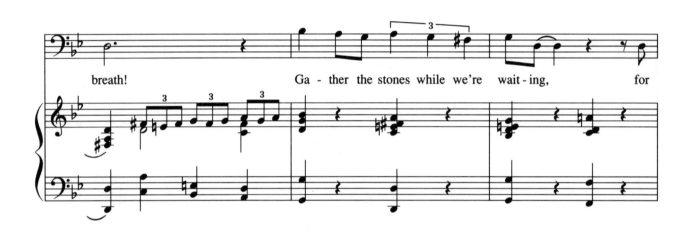

breath! Ga - ther the stones while we're wait-ing, for

soon we shall put her to death!

Refrain

Tenors: Stone her! Stone her!

Take her out and stone her! That's what we should do.

Basses: Stone her! Stone her! That's what we should do. Take her out and

Stone her! Stone her! Take her out and stone her, e - vil through and

stone her, stone her! Stone her! Stone her! E - vil through and

U
Slower - menacing

through! Stone her!

Agitator:

through! Stone her! 4. See how she trem - bles be - fore us,

59

frigh-tened, re-morse-ful and weak! Now she will get what is

com-ing, the Mas-ter is go-ing to speak!

V **Refrain**

Tenors: Stone her! Stone her! Take her out and stone her! That's what we should

Basses: Stone her! Stone her! That's what we should

do.   Stone her! Stone her! Take her out and stone her,

do. Take her out and stone her, stone her! Stone her! Stone her!

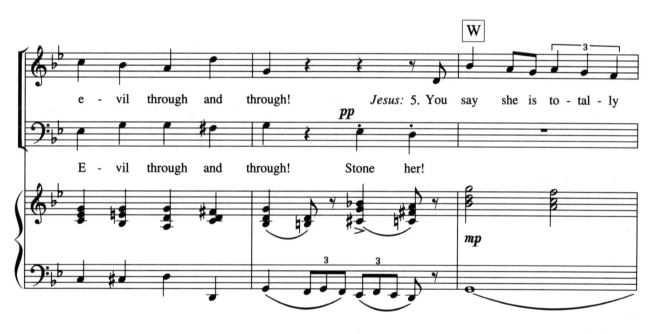

W

e - vil through and through!   *Jesus:* 5. You say she is to - tal - ly

E - vil through and through! Stone her!

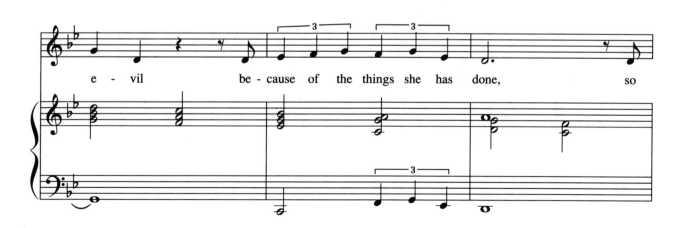

e - vil   be - cause of the things she has done,   so

one who is to - tal - ly sin - less a - mong you may throw the first

stone.

(Stunned silence)

X **Slowly**

Onlooker: 6. Leave her, leave her,

come a - way and leave her. E - ven if she ought to die,

leave her, leave her, leave her, come a - way and leave her, no - one here can

Z *Jesus:*

mf

7. See there is none to con-demn you, and mine is the pow'r to for-

T

p

Leave her, leave her, come a-way and leave her, e - ven if she

B

Leave her, leave her, e - ven if she

p

give, so go from this place and this mo - ment, for

ought to die. Leave her, leave her, come a-way and leave her,

sf

ought to die. Leave her, leave her,

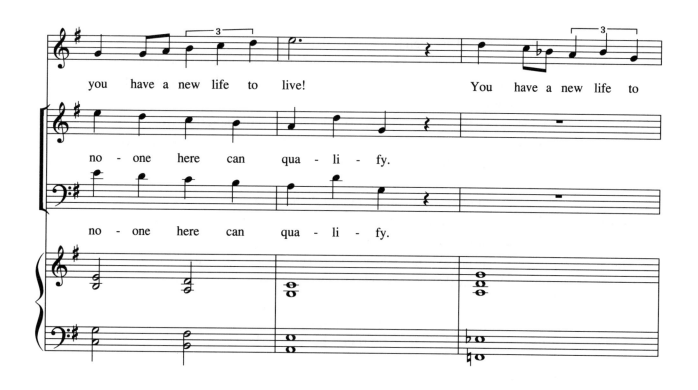

you have a new life to live! You have a new life to

no - one here can qua - li - fy.

no - one here can qua - li - fy.

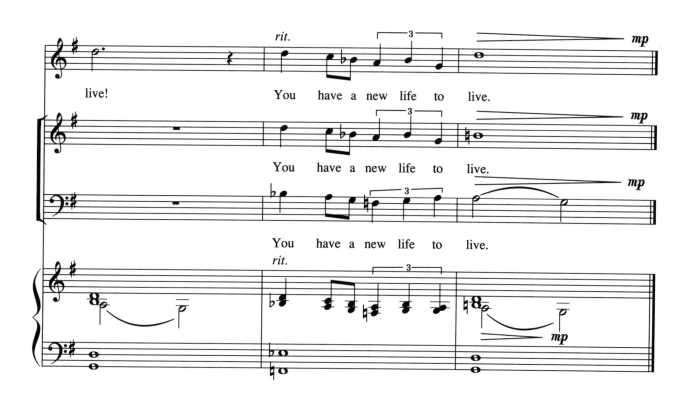

live! You have a new life to live.

You have a new life to live.

You have a new life to live.

▲

Narrator 2:	Well, he seems to have won that one, hands down.
Narrator 1:	Yes - and look at how he did it. He made people take a hard look at themselves, and face up to things they didn't like. They'd come along, full of their own self-righteousness ...
Narrator 2:	And Jesus told them that they weren't as good as they thought they were.
Narrator 1:	No, that's the trouble, he didn't just tell them so, he actually forced them to see it for themselves, admit it and face up to it.
Narrator 2:	Painful!
Narrator 1:	Precisely - so it just made them resent him all the more.
Narrator 2:	All the same - a lot of people must have loved to see it - there's nothing better than to see the self-righteous deflated! I love it!
Narrator 1:	Yes, but you're not so happy when it's *your* self-righteousness, are you? But you're right to say that some people liked it - and that made it even worse.
Narrator 2:	How's that?
Narrator 1:	Well, imagine: you're a church leader, with a good theology degree, and you live very properly, and do all the right things, but people don't seem to listen to you very much.
Narrator 2:	So, what's new?
Narrator 1:	Just a minute. Then along comes this fellow with creased clothes, dirty finger nails and a funny accent, who does all the *wrong* things, and whose only qualification is in carpentry - and when he talks about God, everyone listens to him. How do you feel now?
Narrator 2:	Mmm ... I see what you mean!

11. HE'S JUST A SIMPLE CARPENTER

1. hands.
2. law!
3. mind.
4. dress.

So why do all the peo - ple hang u -
He heals the sick and feeds the hun - gry
I know they say he's worked a so - called
They say he's kept by wo - men, and he

1. pon his ev'- ry word?
2. on the sab - bath day;
3. mi - ra - cle or two,
4. has - n't a - ny shame,

We can't be - lieve the ho - nour he com -
we've ne - ver seen the like of it be -
but they were of a ve - ry doubt - ful
but the peo - ple seem to love him none - the -

ff **Refrain**

1. mands!
2. fore!
3. kind.
4. less!

Chorus: He's on - ly a car - pen - ter,

ff

on - ly a car - pen - ter! He wants to teach the poor to sing and

dance! He's on - ly a car - pen - ter,

on - ly a car - pen - ter! We've got to see he does - n't

Verses 1 - 3 *f* |*Verse 4*

get the chance! *Pharisee:* 2. He's get the chance!
Priest: 3. He's
Roman Official: 4. He's

f

❐

Narrator 1:	The really big crunch came just before the Passover Festival one year, when Jesus went to Jerusalem. He chose to ride into the city on a donkey.
Narrator 2:	Why did he choose to do that? Couldn't he cope with a horse?
Narrator 1:	Some people say he was deliberately being provocative. There's a prophecy in the Old Testament about a new king coming to Jerusalem riding on a donkey.
Narrator 2:	Sounds a bit odd to me - I'd have thought a horse would be more appropriate - or a chariot (not that I know where Jesus would have got one!).
Narrator 1:	That's the point. The prophet was pointing to a different kind of king - someone much more like Jesus, whose power was based on love, not on military strength.
Narrator 2:	Fair enough - that's the kind of person Jesus was, anyway. So it fits.
Narrator 1:	Of course it does, but the people did not see that. They thought he was giving them some kind of coded message, and that the revolution was about to begin. You should have heard the racket - it very nearly started a riot!

12. CRY HOSANNAH!

B

Solo: 1. See him rid-ing to the ci - ty, as the scrip - tures

Solo: 2. Sound the bat - tle cry of free - dom in the pla - ces

Solo: 3. Let the val - leys rise to meet him, turn the hills in -

have fore - told; he will drive the Ro - mans back in -

round a - bout and pre - pare a pro - per high - way

to a plain, ev'- ry hill and moun - tain must be

to the sea! We shall see the great ful - fil - ment

for the Lord, for with Je - sus at the head of

le - velled down, for a wor - thy son of Da - vid

of the pro - phe - cies un - fold, as all of

us to put them all to rout, we'll have no

comes to claim the throne a - gain, and we'll all be

Fewer and fewer voices

One!   Cry ho - san - nah!   Cry ho - san - nah!   Wel - come

Da - vid's roy - al son!   Cry ho - san - nah!   Cry ho_

san - nah!   Bles - sed be the Ho - ly One!   Bles - sed

One or two voices only

be the Ho - ly One!   Cry ho - san - nah!

74

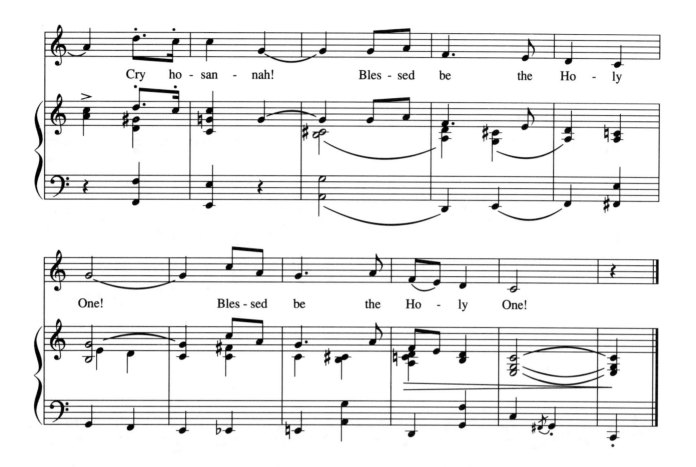

Cry ho - san - nah! Bles - sed be the Ho - ly

One! Bles - sed be the Ho - ly One!

Narrator 2:	What happened to that?
Narrator 1:	Just what you heard - it didn't last - that kind of popular support seldom does.
Narrator 2:	I suppose they realised that he wasn't the kind of person they were expecting.
Narrator 1:	Yes, with a bit more to it. It must have been rather a shock when Jesus got to the temple. They most probably expected him to throw the Romans out. Instead, it was the Jewish traders who got the treatment.
Narrator 2:	What were traders doing there in the first place?
Narrator 1:	Well, people needed special money to pay the temple tax with, and they needed animals and birds for sacrifice. So the traders set up stalls in the temple.
Narrator 2:	A bit like those people who set up flower stalls outside hospitals.
Narrator 1:	Yes, the same sort of idea, except that they were inside the temple, taking up space that was meant for other things.
Narrator 2:	I see - a bit like selling flowers in the operating theatres.
Narrator 1:	If you insist … now, where was I?
Narrator 2:	Trading in the temple.
Narrator 1:	Thank you! Well, Jesus took exception to it and threw them out.
Narrator 2:	Good for him!
Narrator 1:	They didn't say that - and neither did the temple authorities.
Narrator 2:	Well, they wouldn't would they?
Narrator 1:	That might explain why, only a few days later, all that 'hosannah' stuff had changed into something very different.

13. CRUCIFY HIM!

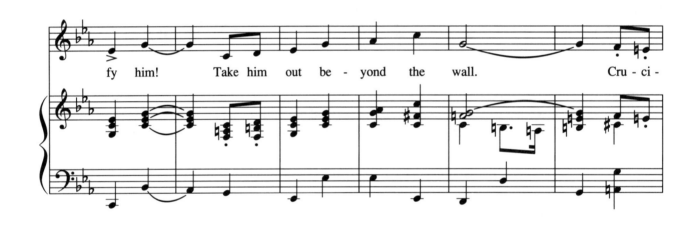

all! Si - lence him for good and all! *Chorus:* Cru - ci -

D

fy him! Cru - ci - fy him! Take him out be - yond the

wall. Cru - ci - fy him! Cru - ci - fy him! Si - lence

him for good and all! Si - lence him for good and

all!

Solo: 1. I was on - ly sell - ing pi - geons, it's not
Solo: 2. I was on - ly chang - ing mo - ney, well, we've
Solo: 3. I was on - ly sell - ing lambs and goats for

much but I get by, and I've ne - ver been com -
got to do it there, since the or - di - na - ry
sa - cri - fi - cial rites, so that peo - ple can ob -

plained a - bout be - fore; when a Spi - rit - filled fa -
coi - nage is pro - fane; when a jumped - up lo - cal
serve the pro - per feast, when this fel - low with a

na - tic with a spar - kle in his eye came
prea - cher came in call - ing us to prayer. We've
whip came in and put them all to flight, and I

fy him! Cru - ci - fy him! Si - lence him for good and
all! Si - lence him for good and all!

▲

Narrator 2:   Well, really! That's quite disgraceful - after all Jesus had done for people, and
               they go and treat him like that.

Narrator 1:   Well, it's not unusual. People really are notoriously fickle. And anyway, it was
               not only the crowd that behaved like that.

Narrator 2:   I know one of the disciples betrayed Jesus - a chap called Judas, wasn't it?

Narrator 1:   Not only him. They all turned out to be pretty unreliable, when push came to
               shove - especially Peter.

Narrator 2:   I'd always thought Peter was a rather special person.

Narrator 1:   He was - but he was mortal, too.

Narrator 2:   So, how did he stand out as a failure?

Narrator 1:   He followed, after Jesus was arrested, and went into the courtyard to listen to
               the trial. People were saying all sorts of things about Jesus which weren't true,
               to try to get a reason to kill him.

Narrator 2:   Didn't Peter stand up for him?

Narrator 1:   Who knows - he might have done, if he hadn't had such an unnerving
               experience.

Narrator 2:   What was that?

Narrator 1:   Well, he was standing warming his hands at the fire, when one of the High
               Priest's household spotted him.

14. I DO NOT KNOW THE MAN!

Urgently

mp

mp staccato

Solo: 1. Look, here is a di-
man was a friend of
know that you were

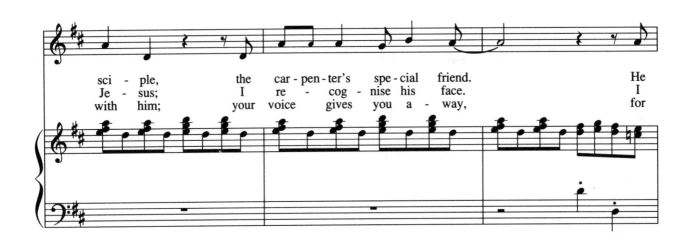

sci - ple, the car-pen-ter's spe-cial friend. He
Je - sus; I re-cog-nise his face. I
with him; your voice gives you a-way, for

swore to fol - low Je - sus un - til the bit - ter
won - der what pos - sessed him to come in - to this
you speak with a nor-thern ac - cent; now, what have you to

mp

night.   He said I would de - ny him, and

I have proved him right. He turns his eyes u -

pon me; I can - not meet his gaze. That

look of love and sor - row will haunt me all my

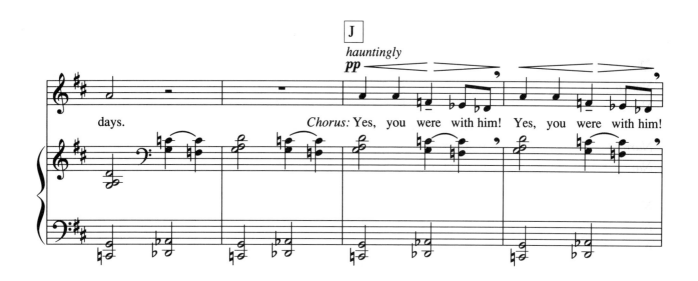

days. *Chorus:* Yes, you were with him! Yes, you were with him!

Yes, you were with him! *Tenor solo:* I do not know the man!

Bass solo: I

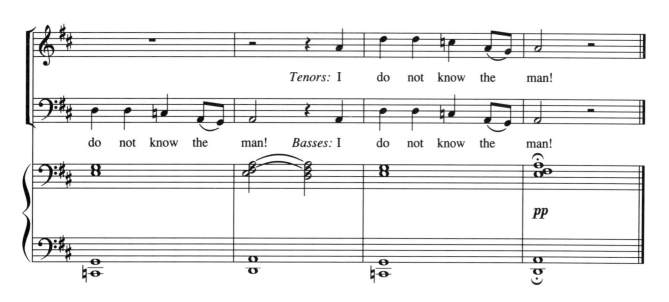

Tenors: I do not know the man!

do not know the man! *Basses:* I do not know the man!

◻

Narrator 2:	So Jesus was left alone.
Narrator 1:	To all intents and purposes. In the end, it was he who had to stand by what he'd said and done, without any help from anyone else.
Narrator 2:	So they crucified him?
Narrator 1:	This was the point of no return. He either had to go back on everything he'd stood for all his life, or he would be crucified.
Narrator 2:	So, being Jesus …
Narrator 1:	He got crucified.
Narrator 2:	But they must have been absolutely barbaric people - to do that to someone, just because he's said and done a few unpopular things. Thank God we've changed a bit now.
Narrator 1:	Have we? I don't think things are so different. And I don't think those people were really so barbaric, either. We all have things we're afraid of - things we don't want to face - either in the world or within ourselves.
Narrator 2:	And when someone makes us face them …
Narrator 1:	We crucify them.
Narrator 2:	I suppose most of us have people we're afraid of, as well - even if it's only double-glazing salesmen.
Narrator 1:	It's more likely to be people with certain kinds of diseases,
Narrator 2:	Or with different lifestyles,
Narrator 1:	Or with different ways of speaking,
Narrator 2:	Or with different colour skins.
Narrator 1:	And when people try to make us face up to our prejudices
Narrator 2:	We get frightened, and sometimes we react in ways that are very unjust.
Narrator 1:	Perhaps we don't actually crucify people, but that's the problem with vendettas. You can begin them very easily, but it's much harder to stop them, and pretty well impossible to control or predict the final outcome.
Narrator 2:	So, those people won, then.
Narrator 1:	No. They *would* have done, if Jesus had given in to them: if he'd changed his preaching, or his lifestyle - or even if he'd lost his temper and told them all what he thought of them.
Narrator 2:	You mean he didn't even do that?
Narrator 1:	Quite the contrary. He prayed for forgiveness for them. And when he was actually dying he seemed far more concerned for other people - including the criminals crucified with him - than for himself.
Narrator 2:	That must have made quite an impression.
Narrator 1:	It seems that it did, although we don't know very much about that, but it must have left a lot of people with more questions than answers.

15. WHAT KIND OF MAN WAS THIS?

Freely, with expression

Mary Magdalene:

What kind of man was this, and how did he of - fend, who taught us

(For rehearsal only)

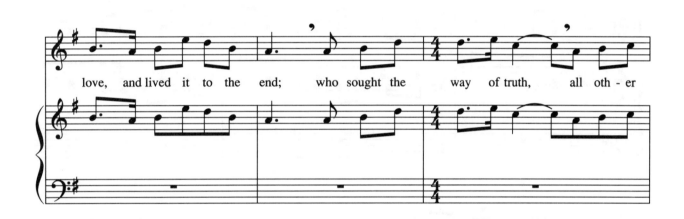

love, and lived it to the end; who sought the way of truth, all oth - er

things a - bove? What kind of man was this, what kind of love? What kind of

Joanna: What kind of

man was this, so full of truth di - vine, who turned the foul - est wa - ter in - to

wine; who called us to his side, and gave us all a place? What kind of

man was this, what kind of grace?

Chorus: What kind of man was this, who o - pened up his

heart to those who sought to tear his flesh a - part; whose all for -

giv - ing words his per - fect na - ture prove? What kind of

What kind of

What kind of

man was this, what kind of love? What kind of

man was this, what kind of love, what kind of love? What kind of

man was this, who helped us all to see the full - ness

man was this, who helped us all to see the full - ness

man was this, who helped us all to see the full - ness

man was this, who helped us all to see the full - ness

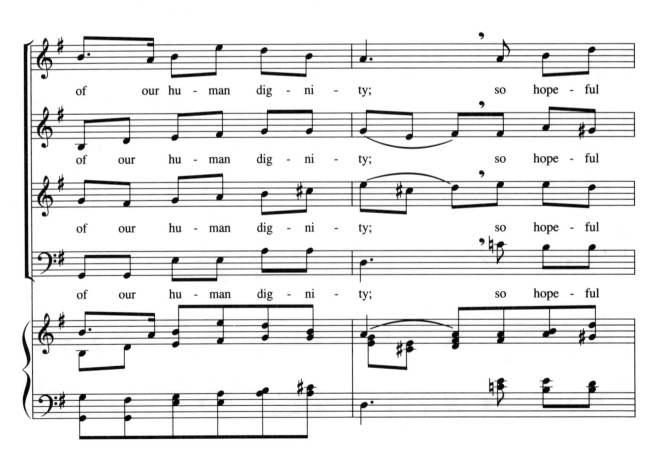

of our hu - man dig - ni - ty; so hope - ful

of our hu - man dig - ni - ty; so hope - ful

of our hu - man dig - ni - ty; so hope - ful

of our hu - man dig - ni - ty; so hope - ful

in des-pair, so no-ble in dis-grace? What kind of

in des-pair, so no-ble in dis - grace? What kind of

in des-pair, so no-ble in dis - grace? What kind of

in des-pair, so no-ble in dis-grace? What kind of

man was this, what kind of grace?

man was this, what kind of grace, what kind of grace?

man was this, what kind of grace, what kind of grace?

man was this, what kind of grace?

91

PART 3: RESURRECTION

(Narrators from darkness)

Narrator 1:	The body of Jesus was taken down from the cross, and put into a stone tomb, which was sealed up and guarded by soldiers.
Narrator 2:	It must have been a dreadful time for the disciples.
Narrator 1:	Two days and a night without hope . . .
Narrator 2:	Without relief from the pain of bereavement and failure...
Narrator 1:	The longest two nights in their lives - until...
Narrator 2:	Until what?

(Here, reading lights come on for the narrators)

Narrator 1:	It began with the women who had followed Jesus to Jerusalem. They'd never really left. They'd seen the crucifixion, and followed to see where Jesus was buried.
Narrator 2:	That was risky.
Narrator 1:	Yes, but if you look at the world now, you'll often find women taking risks.
Narrator 2:	Such as where?
Narrator 1:	Well, in some Latin American countries, where there's poverty and repression, the women have formed into groups to try to end it.
Narrator 2:	Don't they get persecuted?
Narrator 1:	Yes, but they still continue to do it. Rather like the women in this story - they were at the cross, keeping watch, and then on the Sunday morning, very early, they went to the tomb.
Narrator 2:	Whatever for?
Narrator 1:	To annoint the body - they wanted to observe the proper burial procedures.
Narrator 2:	That seems a bit pointless.
Narrator 1:	Well, that's the thing. Sometimes, we need to do things that seem pointless. You can't live life just on a so-called 'rational' level.
Narrator 2:	But how were they going to open the tomb?
Narrator 1:	They didn't know.
Narrator 2:	Come to that, how were they going to get past the guards?
Narrator 1:	They probably hadn't worked that one out, either. Sometimes, if you wait until everything is neatly worked out before you act, you just don't do anything at all.
Narrator 2:	It all sounds a bit haphazard to me.
Narrator 1:	It does, doesn't it. Nevertheless, when they got to the garden, the guard had gone, and the tomb was open.
Narrator 2:	Strange.
Narrator 1:	And it got stranger. It turned out that Jesus was alive.
Narrator 2:	You mean he hadn't died, after all?

Narrator 1:	He'd died, all right. But he'd risen from the dead. The women ran off to tell the men about it.
Narrator 2:	How did they react?
Narrator 1:	The story's a little bit obscure, but it's fairly clear that the men took a lot of convincing.
Narrator 2:	Well, that's not surprising - we sometimes find it difficult to take what women say seriously. They probably thought it was an old wives' tale.
Narrator 1:	Yes, and I bet *that's* an expression men invented, as well.

(Knocking at door - sound effects or percussion instruments)

(Stage lights fully on)

16. HE'S ALIVE, HE'S ALIVE, HE'S ALIVE!

that's what the an - gels said.

Tenors:
1. These wo - men are de - li - ri - ous, that's
2. It's real - ly not sur - pris - ing that their
3. We've got to make al - low - an - ces, we
4. If we car - ry on ig - nor - ing them, per -

that's what the an - gels said.

Basses:
1. These wo - men are de -
2. It's real - ly not sur -
3. We've got to make al -
4. If we car - ry on ig -

mp

1. all there is to say, their heads are full of gos - sip, fad and
2. minds are in a mess they're vic - tims of their own i - ma - gi -
3. must - n't be un - kind, the last few days have left their sen - ses
4. haps they'll go a - way. We've said be - fore, and we shall say a -

1. li - ri - ous, that's all there is to say, their heads are full of
2. pri - sing that their minds are in a mess they're vic - tims of their
3. low - an - ces, we must - n't be un - kind, the last few days have
4. nor - ing them, per - haps they'll go a - way. We've said be - fore, and

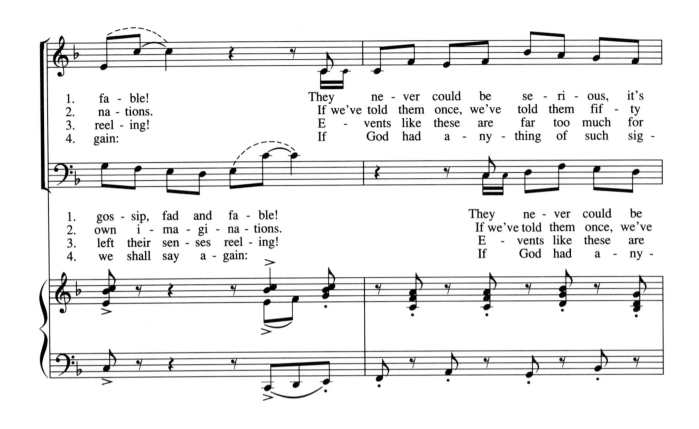

1. fa - ble!   They   ne - ver could   be   se - ri - ous, it's
2. na - tions.   If we've told them once, we've told them fif - ty
3. reel - ing!   E - vents like these are   far   too much for
4. gain: If   God had   a - ny - thing of such   sig -

1. gos - sip, fad and fa - ble!   They   ne - ver could be
2. own i - ma - gi - na - tions.   If we've told them once, we've
3. left their sen - ses reel - ing!   E - vents like these are
4. we shall say a - gain: If   God had   a - ny -

1. sim - ply not their way,   they're   na - tu - ral - ly   fligh - ty and un -
2. thou - sand times, not   less,   to   curb their in - fan - tile ex - ag - ge -
3. a - ny wo - man's mind,   we've   got to un - der - stand the way they're
4. ni - fi - cance to say,   he'd have said it to some   le - vel - hea - ded

1. se - ri - ous, it's sim - ply not their   way,   they're na - tu - ral - ly
2. told them fif - ty thou - sand times, not   less,   to   curb their in - fan -
3. far   too much for   a - ny wo - man's   mind,   we've got to un - der -
4. thing of such sig - ni - fi - cance to   say,   he'd have said it to some

98

Refrain M

1. sta - ble! *Sopranos and Altos:* He's a - live, he's a - live! He is ri - sen from the dead. He's a -
2. ra - tion!
3. feel - ing!
4. men!

1. fligh - ty and un - sta - ble!
2. tile ex - ag - ge - ra - tion!
3. stand the way they're feel - ing!
4. le - vel hea - ded men!

live, he's a - live, yes a - live! He's a - live, he's a - live, he is

S ri - sen from the dead. Ah,

A ri - sen from the dead. That's what the an - gels said, ah,

help them draw the line, and drink-ing al-ways means —

(stunned silence)

di - sci - pline to help them draw the line, and drink-ing al-ways means —

(stunned silence)

O **Slowly**

Jesus: Peace be with you!

(with Sopranos and Altos second time)

Tenors: He's a - live, he's a - live! He is

Basses: He's a - live, he's a - live! He is

Ah, that's what we've al - ways

said, ah, that's what we've al - ways

said. Tenors, Sopranos & Altos: He's a - said.

said. Basses: He's a - said.

rit.

L.H.
pp

Ped.

Narrator 2:	That's a bit unjust!
Narrator 1:	Yes. The bible clearly says that women were the first to believe and proclaim the resurrection, but it also indicates that it wasn't long before the men were acting as though it had been them!
Narrator 2:	I suppose in a sense it's always been a man's world.
Narrator 1:	I don't know about 'always', but for a long time the customs and traditions have tended to favour men.
Narrator 2:	And we all know how people love to cling on to the way things have always been.
Narrator 1:	That's right. There's no more powerful argument for not doing something new than …
Narrator 2:	'It's never been done before',
Narrator 1:	Or, 'This is the way we've always done it'.
Narrator 2:	And that goes for our prejudices just as much as for anything else.
Narrator 1:	Yes, it does. But after the resurrection Jesus made it clear that we had to expect new things.
Narrator 2:	So does that mean that we shouldn't value the past - what about all those wonderful traditions?
Narrator 1:	No, the past is very important. But we mustn't be so anxious to hold on to it that we stop anything new from happening.
Narrator 2:	So where does Jesus say that?
Narrator 1:	D'you remember the story about how Jesus met Mary Magdalene in the garden, just after the resurrection?

17. DO NOT TOUCH

Gently

Mary Magdalene: 1. I met him in the gar - den in the ear - ly mor - ning
wan - ted to hold on - to things the way they were be -
ri - sen, and he's with us in a form we can - not

light, but I thought he was the man who worked the land,
fore, but he said that was - n't how it ought to be.
grasp, and with life the u - ni - verse can - not con - tain.

'till I heard   him call me 'Ma — ry' in his own   fa - mi - liar
The   past   is now the   past,   and there are   bet — ter things in
And   not   with nails or   doc - trines, or a   mul — ti - tude of

way,   and I   saw the wound   still   o - pen in   his   hand.
store,   and   that is why   his   spi - rit must   be   free.
words,   will   peo - ple e - ver   pin him down   a - gain!

Refrain Q

Mary Magdalene: 1.
Chorus: 2. 'Do not touch,   do not hold,   do not cling,'   he
Chorus: 3.

said,   'For I give you   a   new song to   sing,'   he

said,   'And   this   is   the   word   you   shall   bring,'   he

said.   'The   Lord   is   ri - sen   in - deed!'

Mary Magdalene: 2. I
Mary Magdalene: 3. He's

Narrator 2:	So, let me get this straight. The resurrection doesn't mean that everything's going to be the way it was?
Narrator 1:	It certainly doesn't. That's a mistake that's often made.
Narrator 2:	Well, what is it about, then?
Narrator 1:	It's about *new* life - not just more of the old.
Narrator 2:	So does that mean that what's gone is not important?
Narrator 1:	No, because the new grows out of the old. There is a continuity.
Narrator 2:	So, what's the difference, then?
Narrator 1:	Seen as you suggest, the resurrection would say that this life is not important. So the resurrection becomes a kind of escape-route, by which to avoid the painful realities of life.
Narrator 2:	So what's wrong with wanting to do that?

Narrator 1:	It's quite a natural thing to want to do. The problem is that avoiding reality doesn't change it. So it's the way to despair. But the resurrection of Jesus helps us to face painful realities and deal with them.
Narrator 2:	So that they can be changed.
Narrator 1:	Yes, very often it's from within the hurts of life that healing comes - like when two people were walking away from Jerusalem on that Sunday evening, towards a nearby town called Emmaus.
Narrator 2:	Running away from the pain?
Narrator 1:	Perhaps that's a slightly unfair way to express it; Emmaus was where they lived. But I'm sure they were not at all sorry to get away from Jerusalem.
Narrator 2:	Not a nice place to be.
Narrator 1:	Lots of bad memories.
Narrator 2:	Not to mention the danger.
Narrator 1:	There are times when we all need to get away from those things for a while.
Narrator 2:	But we can't avoid them for ever.
Narrator 1:	No, but a break sometimes helps us to sort things out a bit. And it wasn't very long before they were back in Jerusalem, panting for breath, and with a most amazing story to tell.

18. GOT TO GET AWAY (Jerusalem Blues)

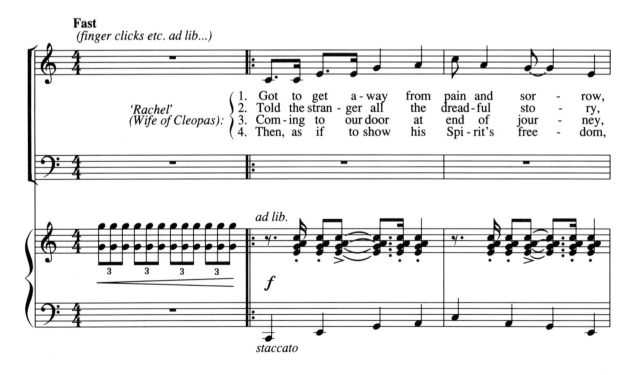

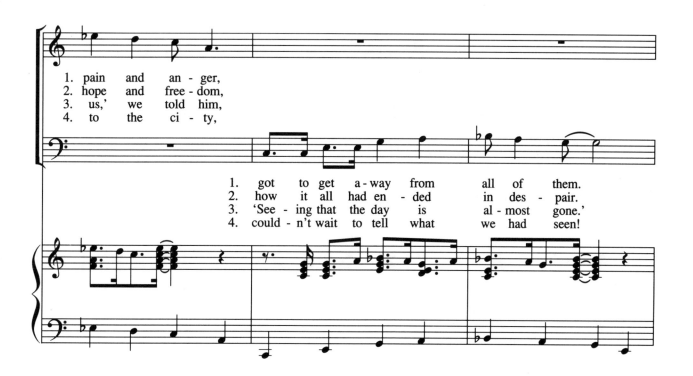

109

1. Walk - ing on the road we met a stran - ger,
2. Stran - ger o - pened up the scrip - tures for us,
3. Sit - ting at our ta - ble, shar - ing sup - per,
4. Got to hur - ry back to where we came from,

1. did - n't seem to know what
2. showed us how it had been
3. stran - ger took and blessed and
4. got to face a - gain the

1. made us tell a - gain the dread - ful sto - ry,
2. Ser - vant of the Lord would have to suf - fer,
3. of - fered it to us, and then we knew him
4. got to tell the news that lights the dark - ness,

1. had oc - cured,
2. pro - phe - sied;
3. broke the bread,
4. place of pain;

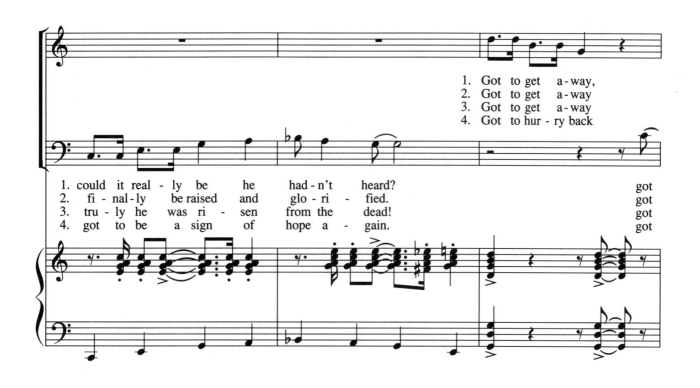

1. Got to get a - way,
2. Got to get a - way
3. Got to get a - way
4. Got to hur - ry back

1. could it real - ly be he had - n't heard?
2. fi - nal - ly be raised and glo - ri - fied.
3. tru - ly he was ri - sen from the dead!
4. got to be a sign of hope a - gain.

got
got
got
got

1. got to get a - way from Je - ru - sa - lem!
2. got to get a - way from Je - ru - sa - lem!
3. got to get a - way from Je - ru - sa - lem!
4. got to hur - ry back to Je - ru - sa - lem!

1. to get a - way, got to get a - way from Je - ru - sa - lem!
2. to get a - way, got to get a - way from Je - ru - sa - lem!
3. to get a - way, got to get a - way from Je - ru - sa - lem!
4. to hur - ry back, got to hur - ry back to Je - ru - sa - lem!

111

Refrain

R *Chorus:*

All: 1. Got to get a-way, got to get a-way, got to get a-way from Je-
2. Got to get a-way, got to get a-way, got to get a-way from Je-
3. Got to get a-way, got to get a-way, got to get a-way from Je-
4. Got to hur-ry back, got to hur-ry back, got to hur-ry back to Je-

Verses 1-3 | **Verse 4**

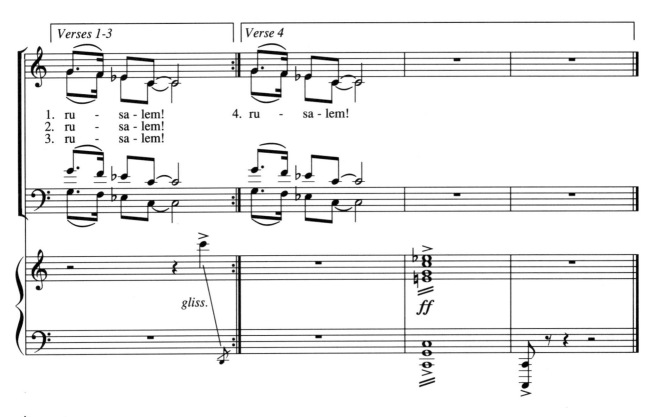

1. ru - sa - lem!
2. ru - sa - lem!
3. ru - sa - lem!

4. ru - sa - lem!

gliss.

ff

* May be sung in unison

Narrator 2:	It sounds to me as though all these appearances were not merely accidental.
Narrator 1:	What do you mean by that?
Narrator 2:	It sounds as though they all had a purpose. When people met Jesus, they learned something new.
▲ *Narrator 1:*	Absolutely, and the same's true now.
Narrator 2:	That could be rather a mixed blessing.
Narrator 1:	It is. People don't always want to learn what he wants to teach.
Narrator 2:	Why do I get the feeling you're about to give me an example?
Narrator 1:	I can't imagine! But since you're obviously looking for one...
Narrator 2:	Go on then!
Narrator 1:	Xenophobia.
Narrator 2:	Who does he play for?
Narrator 1:	Xenophobia - fear of foreigners. Jesus didn't have much time for it.
Narrator 2:	As you'd expect.
Narrator 1:	But the society of his day was riddled with it.
Narrator 2:	And now you're going to tell me that the resurrection said something about that.
Narrator 1:	Well, if you know already...
Narrator 2:	No, go on - you've started, so you'd better finish.
Narrator 1:	I imagine you've heard the expression, 'There's plenty more fish in the sea'?
Narrator 2:	Your imagination does you credit - but what's that got to do with anything?
Narrator 1:	Well, Jesus gave it a whole new meaning.
Narrator 2:	You're not going to tell me it's an old Jewish proverb?
Narrator 1:	I wouldn't know - but the Jewish people of that time knew of a number of different species of fish - a hundred and fifty-three, in fact.
Narrator 2:	You're a mine of irrelevant information, aren't you!
Narrator 1:	Not entirely irrelevant. There's a story about Jesus meeting his disciples when they were fishing, and helping them to catch a remarkable number of fish. I don't suppose you could hazard a guess at how many?

19. ONE HUNDRED AND FIFTY-THREE!

hun - dred and fif - ty three!

Solo:
1. We'd fished all the night for no - thing, but
2. We got all the fish to the shore; we
3. Now here was a won - der - ful sight we'd

mf

Je - sus said 'Try once more.' So we doubt - ful - ly tried on the
won - dered how ma - ny there'd be. We star - ted to count, and
ne - ver ex - pec - ted to see. And the net did - n't break; it was

f **Refrain**

Chorus: One hun - dred and fif - ty -

o - ther side, and found there were fish ga - lore!
what an a - mount: one hun - dred and fif - ty - three!
a - ble to take the hun - dred and fif - ty - three!

f

three!

The num-ber of all the

One hun-dred and fif - ty - three!

fish in the sea: one hun-dred and fif - ty - three!

mf

T

Slowly

mf

Solo: 4. So, whe-ther you're rich or you're

poor, what - e - ver your race or your sect, be you black, white or brown, Je - sus

a tempo   *f* **Refrain**

Chorus: One hun-dred and fif - ty -

wants you a-round; there's plen-ty of room in the net!

three!

One hun-dred and fif - ty - three!

The num-ber of all the

fish in the sea: one hun-dred and fif - ty - three! One

hun-dred and fif - ty - three! One hun-dred and fif - ty - three! The

num-ber of all the fish in the sea: one hun-dred and fif - ty - three!

Narrator 2:	So you're saying that there's plenty of room for everybody, and no-one needs to be left out.
Narrator 1:	I think you've got it!
Narrator 2:	But what does it mean, practically, here and now? If I say I want to follow Jesus, what does it mean?
Narrator 1:	That's a big question - but let me ask you one: what's the most important thing about Jesus, from what you've just heard?
Narrator 2:	Well, he loved life - and celebrated it.
Narrator 1:	What else?
Narrator 2:	He enabled others to celebrate it - especially those that tended to get left out.
Narrator 1:	Right. So, if we want to follow him, we have to say that life is good, and that it's meant to be good for everybody, and not just for the privileged few.
Narrator 2:	*They* won't like that.
Narrator 1:	No, and I never said that it would bring you easy popularity. It might produce the same kind of mixed reaction he experienced.
Narrator 2:	So it might get uncomfortable.
Narrator 1:	It might.
Narrator 2:	So why do it?
Narrator 1:	Because, when all else is said and done, the gospel is about life. And none of us can really have life while others are denied it. So we're announcing life in all its fullness for everybody.
Narrator 2:	O.K. - so you've convinced me. But there's still a question.
Narrator 1:	Go on.
Narrator 2:	It's easy to say, 'Follow Jesus', but where do I find him? I've got an idea of what it's about, now, but you say he's actually alive. So where is he?
Narrator 1:	Well, he said that when we helped people who needed help - people who are pushed aside, people who are … I'll tell you what, why don't I ask some of these people to tell you where *they* have met him?
Narrator 2:	I thought you'd never ask!

20. FINALE: SINGING, DANCING CARPENTER (4)

Solo: 1. The

1. car - pen - ter is danc - ing yet, and still he sings his song; he
2. met him in the hun - gry, and we took the time to care; we
3. met him as a stran - ger, in a coun - try not his own, a
4. met him as a hos - tage with a ran - som on his head, or
5. met him in the cold with - out a shirt u - pon his back, a
6. meet him in the hun - gry, in the lone - ly and the sad, we

1. calls us all to sing with him and move the dance a - long; and
2. gave our time and e - ner - gy, to make the world more fair. A
3. con - su - lar em - bar - rass - ment, un - wan - ted and a - lone; we
4. wrong - ly put in pri - son for the things he did and said; we
5. D. S. S. sta - tis - tic, at the bot - tom of the stack, we
6. e - ven re - cog - nise him in the folk we think are bad; the

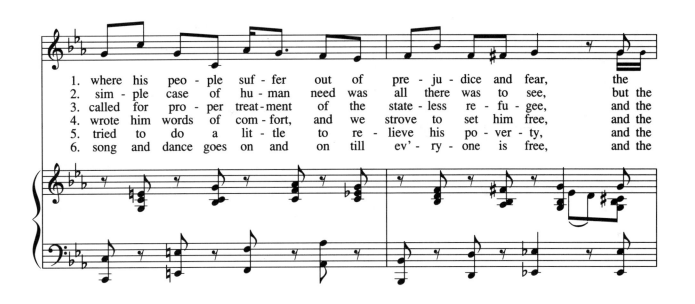

1. where his peo - ple suf - fer out of pre - ju - dice and fear, the
2. sim - ple case of hu - man need was all there was to see, but the
3. called for pro - per treat - ment of the state - less re - fu - gee, and the
4. wrote him words of com - fort, and we strove to set him free, and the
5. tried to do a lit - tle to re - lieve his po - ver - ty, and the
6. song and dance goes on and on till ev' - ry - one is free, and the

Refrain
Chorus & Audience

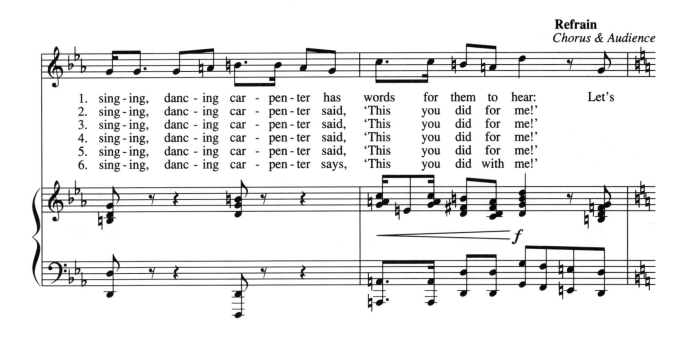

1. sing - ing, danc - ing car - pen - ter has words for them to hear: Let's
2. sing - ing, danc - ing car - pen - ter said, 'This you did for me!'
3. sing - ing, danc - ing car - pen - ter said, 'This you did for me!'
4. sing - ing, danc - ing car - pen - ter said, 'This you did for me!'
5. sing - ing, danc - ing car - pen - ter said, 'This you did for me!'
6. sing - ing, danc - ing car - pen - ter says, 'This you did with me!'

sing with the car - pen - ter till peace and jus - tice spread; let's

121

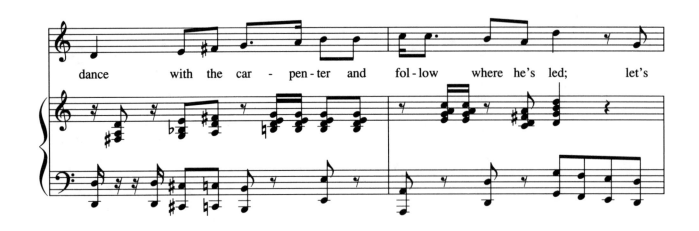

dance   with the car - pen - ter and   fol - low   where he's led;   let's

sing   and dance for free - dom, see   the   poor and hun - gry   fed,   pro -

Verses 1 - 5

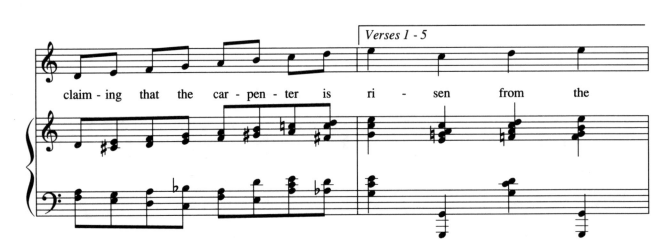

claim - ing that   the   car - pen - ter is   ri -   sen   from   the

dead!

Solo: 2. We
Solo: 3. We
Solo: 4. We
Solo: 5. We
Solo: 6. We

Verse 6 *rit.*

ri - sen from the dead!

Notes on Performance

This work may be performed in a variety of different ways, according to the resources available. We prefer to leave as much as possible to the creative talents of the individual producers and musical directors, so there are minimal directions included in the text. However, a few general observations may be useful.

1.   The piece will work best if a good visual impact is achieved by the use of dance and possibly mime, though it works well as a straightforward cantata. We would like to think that it could also be used as a useful mine for seasonal anthems or worship songs. To make the work even more flexible, a fully-staged supplement is available from the publisher, including additional dialogue and music. This enables it to be performed as a full-scale dramatic production.

2.   It is strongly to be recommended that churches or schools combine with other organisations - local dance or drama groups could be included, for example, to make the production a real community activity. This would certainly be pleasing to the Singing, Dancing Carpenter himself, and in the spirit of his ministry!

3.   If resources permit, the characters could be acted on stage by those singing the parts, and much fun could be had in the making of costumes, sets, etc. However, the dialogue and the songs are intended to make clear connections with the present day. Therefore we would suggest that any sets or costumes should be contemporary in style.

4.   An alternative way of performing the work would be to have the soloists singing from within the chorus, perhaps at the back of the stage, with dance and/or mime artists representing the characters visually. Several characters could be sung by one singer, reducing the total number of soloists.

5.   The verses of the songs can be sung either as solos or by small groups of singers. Try and persuade as many people as possible to sing a solo verse or two - see the table of contents for our suggestions, all of which are totally flexible. The solo verses have been written with the 'average', enthusiastic chorus singer in mind - nothing should be too high or too low, or too difficult!

6.   In many songs, the soloists are not named, again allowing flexibility in the combining of roles, if desired. Where consistency is a consideration, names have been given. Generally, these are the actual biblical names of the characters represented, but in one or two instances where names are not known, they have been invented. In those cases, the name is distinguished by being in inverted commas.

7.   Audience participation is certainly to be encouraged. The necessary rehearsal time before the performance will certainly be regarded as part of the fun, and will also be more than repaid in the enjoyment of the actual work. It is recommended that the refrain from the theme song in its various forms (numbers 1, 7, 9 and 20) be used in this way, but it need not end here. It might well be healthy for us to recognise ourselves in singing any of the other choruses (particularly numbers 2, 5, 12, 13 and 19).

8.   There is no 'set' orchestration for the music in *Singing, Dancing Carpenter*. Here again there can be total flexibility in performance. The piano/keyboard part provided in the vocal score can stand on its own, or can be augmented by any number of available instruments. A 'flexi-pack' set of instrumental parts is available separately, from the publisher.

9.   We hope this work will be enjoyed in its entirety, but, if it is absolutely necessary to shorten the work, we would suggest omitting some verses from the longer numbers. If complete numbers need to be cut, we would suggest numbers 5a, 11, 14, and 19. These are marked in the text by a ▲ at the start of the cut and ◻ at the end.

Michael Forster
Christopher Tambling